Sylvester

THE MOUSE WITH
THE MUSICAL EAR

A Golden Beginning Reader

BY ADELAIDE HOLL
ILLUSTRATED BY N. M. BODECKER

GOLDEN PRESS
NEW YORK

1969 Edition

Sylvester was a country mouse.
He lived in a grassy meadow,
and there were lovely sounds
all about him.

On the north there was a little road
where birds fluttered in the dust
and made little chirping sounds.

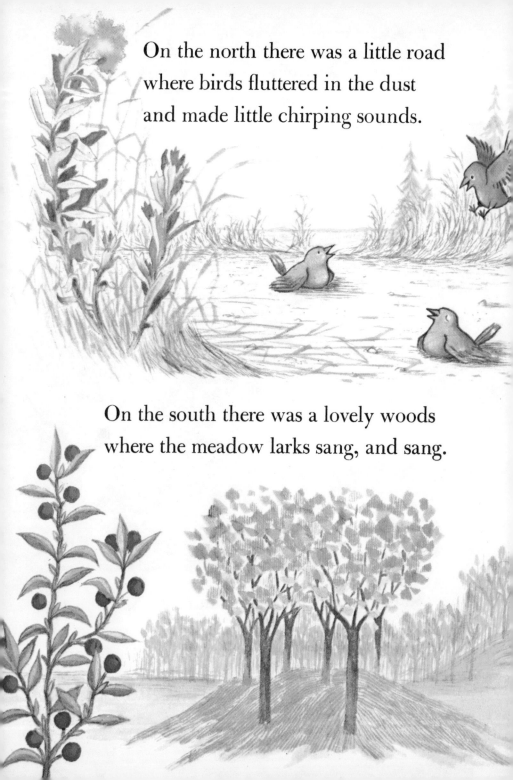

On the south there was a lovely woods
where the meadow larks sang, and sang.

On the east there was a cornfield
where soft winds made music all day,
and crickets chirp, chirped all night.

And on the west there was a silver brook
that went gurgle, glub, glub!
with a musical beat.

7

Sylvester was a mouse
with a musical ear.
He loved the meadow sounds by day.

He loved the meadow sounds by night.
He would sit in his doorway,
listening to the birds and to the crickets.
He would sit, listening
to the winds and to the brook.
He would sit, quiet,
humming softly to himself.

9

But one day men came from the city.
They dug up the little road on the north
and made a big highway.
Now, birds no longer fluttered in the dust
and made little chirping sounds.
Cars went by ZOOM!
Trucks went by WHOOSH!
Sylvester no longer heard
the music of the birds.

Soon down the big highway
the city began to come closer.
One day men came and cut down
the lovely woods on the south.
They put up rows and rows of houses.
Now the meadow larks
no longer sang in the woods.
The meadow larks went away
to sing and sing in another place.

And the city came closer and closer.
Men came once more.
They cut down the cornfield on the east
and put up rows and rows of shops.
The crickets went away
to chirp, chirp in another cornfield.
And Sylvester no longer heard the winds
above the city noises.

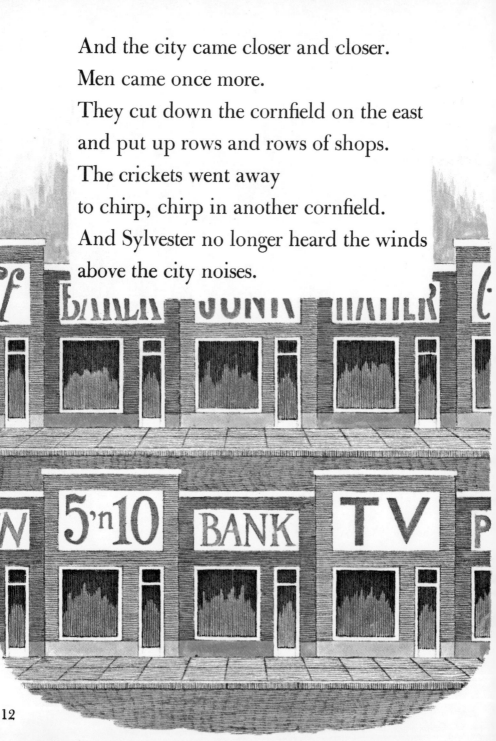

The city came closer and closer.

Men came again.

They dug up the silver brook on the west.

Now, it no longer went gurgle, glub, glub!
with a musical beat.

And Sylvester no longer sat in his doorway
humming softly to himself.

He just sat,

listening to the ZOOM! of the cars

and the WHOOSH! of the trucks.

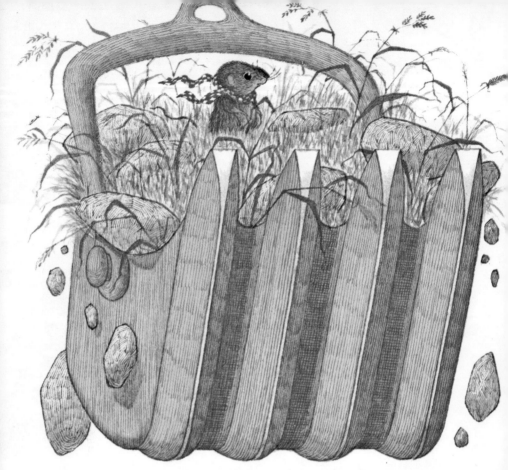

One day men came with a big bulldozer.
They dug up the grassy meadow.
They dug up Sylvester's house.
They even dug up Sylvester.
"I am no longer a country mouse.
I am a city mouse," he said.
"I shall find another home."
And away he went.

There were many places in the city.
But no place was just right
for a mouse with a musical ear.
Some places were too noisy.
And some places were too quiet.
Sylvester went on and on.

All at once he heard lovely sounds.
He heard lovely music. In he went.
And there was a place
filled with musical sounds.
There was a place just right
for a mouse with a musical ear.

Sylvester saw a fine house.
There was a little door
for going in, and for coming out.
Across the doorway was a wire fence.
In went Sylvester, and he sat, quiet,
humming softly to himself.

Sylvester liked his house.
He especially liked the gay music—
piano music, violin music,
and drums with a musical beat.
Sylvester liked his doorway.
He especially liked going in,
and coming out.
When he went across the wire fence,
he made lovely sounds. Plink! Plink!
He made music.

Sylvester was very quiet by day.
But at night, when the shop was dark,
he played on the wire fence
across his doorway.
He played quiet music. Plink! Plink!
He played noisy music. Plonk! Plonk!
He played the music he heard all day.

People went by the shop at night.
"Who is playing?" they asked.
"Who plays music in your shop at night?"
they asked the shopkeeper.

One night the shopkeeper
listened in the dark.
He was very quiet.
Sylvester came softly to his door.

He began to play. Plunk! Plunk! Plunk!
The shopkeeper heard the music.
It came from the guitar on the shelf.
But in the dark he did not see Sylvester.
"It is a magic guitar!" he cried.
"A magic guitar that plays by itself!"

Soon people heard
about the magic guitar.
They stood outside the shop at night
and listened.

They went inside the shop by day
and looked.
But nobody would buy the guitar.
Nobody would buy a magic guitar
that played by itself.

Far away in the West, Tex heard
about the magic guitar.
Tex loved music. Tex loved to sing.
But Tex did not have a guitar.
"A guitar is just what I need," said Tex.
"Especially a magic guitar
that plays by itself!"

Away to the city went Tex.
He traveled a long, long way.
He traveled along, singing as he went.

Finally he came to the city.
"Where can I find the magic guitar?"
he asked.
Tex found the magic guitar.
He bought the magic guitar.
Tex was very happy.

Tex set off for the West
with his magic guitar.
He traveled along, singing as he went.
Inside the guitar was Sylvester
sound asleep.
Tex stopped at night to rest
in a grassy meadow.
It was very dark and very quiet.
All at once Tex heard music.
Plink! Plink! Plunk! Plunk! Plonk! Plonk!

Tex sat up, and there was Sylvester!
"It is not a magic GUITAR!" cried Tex.
"It is a magic MOUSE!
A mouse with a musical ear!"
Sylvester stopped playing.
He saw the lovely grassy meadow.
He heard the lovely country sounds.
He looked and looked at Tex.
At once, he and Tex liked one another.
They became great friends.

Sylvester went home with Tex.
He played the guitar while Tex sang.
They made lovely music together.
People came from far away to listen.
They traveled here,
and they traveled there.
They made soft music and noisy music.

Sylvester traveled
inside his fine house.
And sometimes at night
he would sit, quiet, in his doorway,
humming softly to himself.
Sometimes he was a city mouse,
and sometimes he was a country mouse.
But, at all times,
he was a musical mouse—
a mouse with a musical ear!